Snowy
CHRISTMAS
STICKER ACTIVITY BOOK

Have fun completing the sticker and doodling activities! Look at the sticker sheets. Can you find a sticker that fits? When you are sure you have found the right sticker, carefully peel it off and stick it down. There are also cute press-outs and extra stickers to use anywhere you want!

make believe ideas

Merry maze

Find a way through the maze to the finish.

Add stickers.

Scribble snowball faces!

Start

Finish

Sorting presents

Find the missing stickers, then colour the elf in his new car.

4

Dazzling lights!

Sticker and colour beautiful lights.

Colour Santa's hat, too.

Join the dots.

2 •   • 1
8 •   • 7
14 •   • 13
19 •
15 •   • 18   • 12   • 6
3 •   9 •   20
16   17
10   11
4   5

Start

Finish

5

Find a way through
the tree maze.

Tree toppers

Use colour and stickers to decorate the trees.

Circle the pair of baubles that match.

Counting toys

Count the toys in each sack
then tick the correct number.

2 1 9 6 3

5 3 10 4 8

10 6 8 3 9

5 2 6 9 1

Christmas baking!

Use colour and stickers to decorate
the gingerbread house.

Ingredients

1 gegs

2 rolfu

3 kilm

Find the stickers to unscramble the words.

Decorate the biscuits and colour the cakes.

Woodland wonder

Help the owl through the maze to reach the rabbit.

Start

Sticker the objects found in the maze.

Finish

Busy Santa!

Sticker Santa and the stars, then colour the town.

11

Frosty friends

Find the missing stickers then colour the tree decorations.

Use your stickers to finish the snowmen.

14

Perfect presents

Sticker the missing pets, then follow the lines to find a present for each of them!

Colour the puppy's bean bag.

Merry and bright!

15

Add colour and stickers to complete the scene.

Yummy treats

Circle six differences between
the gingerbread houses.

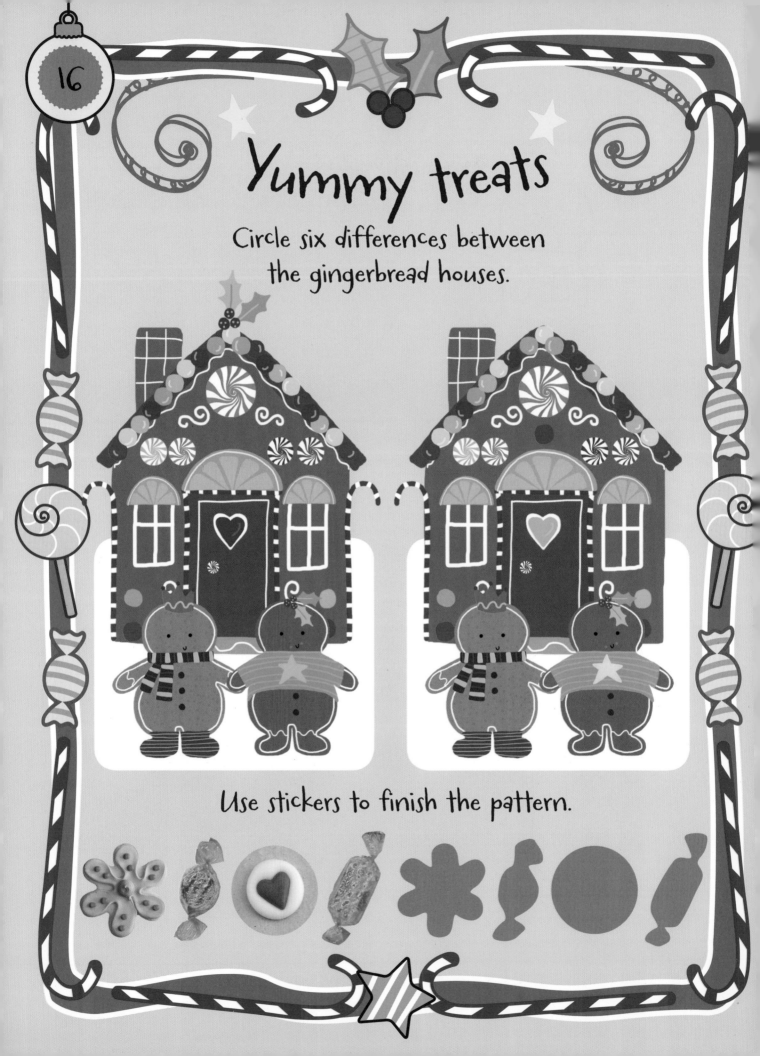

Use stickers to finish the pattern.

Festive ornaments

Press out and decorate the ornaments. Ask an adult to help you thread string through the holes, and then hang your decorations.

Christmas door hanger

Press out and decorate
the door hanger.

MY ROOM